DINOSAURS

INSTRUCTIONS

1 Carefully remove the viewer from the book along the perforated edge. Gently push each side of the viewer inward. Then push the front of the viewer into place.

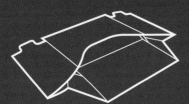

2 Download PI VR Dinosaurs, available on the App Store or Google Play. Direct links to the store locations are found at: pilbooks.com/PIVRDinosaurs.

3 Launch the app. If you are asked to calibrate the viewer, go to page 48 and follow the instructions found there. If asked, allow the app to take photos/videos.

4 After calibrating your viewer, you will be prompted to scan the QR code found to the right to verify your possession of this book.

5 You will see a double image of a dinosaur dig on your phone. Insert your smartphone into the front compartment of the VR viewer. The line between the two images should line up with the notch at the center point of the viewer, between the two lenses. If your screen seems blurry, make sure the smartphone is aligned precisely with the center of the viewer. Adjusting the phone left or right a few millimeters can make a big difference. The tilt of the viewer and the phone can also affect how the screen looks to you.

6 Look around to explore! PI VR Dinosaurs does not require a lever or remote control. You control each interaction with your gaze. When you see a loading circle, keep your gaze focused until it loads fully to access videos, slideshows, and games.

Loading

7 Gaze at the X to close out of video, slideshow, or game screens.

Exit

pil
Publications International, Ltd.

Get the App!

This book is enhanced by an app that can be downloaded from the App Store or Google Play*. Apps are available to download at no cost. Once you've downloaded the app to your smartphone**, use the QR code found on page 1 of this book to access an immersive, 360˚ virtual reality environment. Then slide the phone into the VR viewer and you're ready to go.

Compatible Operating Systems

- Android 4.1 (JellyBean) or later

- iOS 8.0 or later

Compatible Phones

The app is designed to work with smartphones with a screen size of up to 6 inches. Removing your device from its case may provide a better fit in the viewer. If your smartphone meets the above operating system requirements and has gyroscope functionality it should support GoogleVR. Publications International, Ltd. has developed and tested this software with the following devices:

- Google Nexus 5, Google Nexus 5X, Google Nexus 6P, Google Pixel

- Apple iPhone 6, Apple iPhone 6S, Apple iPhone 6 Plus, Apple iPhone 6S Plus, Apple iPhone 7, Apple iPhone 7 Plus

- Samsung Galaxy S5, Samsung Galaxy S5 Active, Samsung Galaxy S5 Sport, Samsung Galaxy S6, Samsung Galaxy S6 edge, Samsung Galaxy S6 edge +, Samsung Galaxy Note 4, Samsung Galaxy Note edge, Samsung Galaxy S7, Samsung Galaxy S7 edge, Samsung Galaxy Note 5, Samsung Galaxy S8

Caution

The viewer should not be exposed to moisture or extreme temperatures. The viewer is not water resistant. It is potentially combustible if the lenses are left facing a strong light source.

Cover art from Shutterstock.com.

Interior art from Encyclopædia Britannica, Inc., National Park Service, and Shutterstock.com.

App content from Encyclopædia Britannica, Inc., Filament Games, Library of Congress, and Shutterstock.com.

Louis Weber, CEO
Publications International, Ltd.
8140 Lehigh Avenue
Morton Grove, IL 60053

Permission is never granted for commercial purposes.

 Publications International, Ltd.

For inquiries email: customer_service@pubint.com

ISBN: 978-1-64030-695-0

Manufactured in China.

8 7 6 5 4 3 2 1

*We reserve the right to terminate the apps.
**Smartphone not included. Standard data rates may apply to download. Once downloaded, the app does not use data or require Wi-Fi access.

CONTENTS

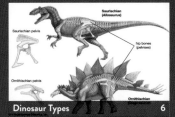

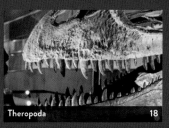

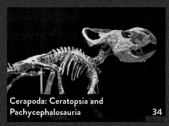

INTRODUCTION

The reptiles known as dinosaurs were the dominant land animals on Earth during most of the Mesozoic Era (252 to 66 million years ago). They thrived for nearly 180 million years. They included meat eaters and plant eaters, animals who walked on two legs and on four, and animals with a solitary lifestyle and those who lived in a herd. Dinosaurs ranged in size from smaller than a chicken to more than 10 times larger than the largest elephant. Dinosaurs were the ancient relatives of today's crocodiles, snakes, lizards, and birds.

FAST FACTS

1. The remains or traces of dinosaurs were first discovered in the early 19th century.

2. Dinosaur fossils have been found on every continent, including Antarctica.

3. At least 1,000 species of dinosaur have been identified.

JURASSIC PERIOD

145 million years ago

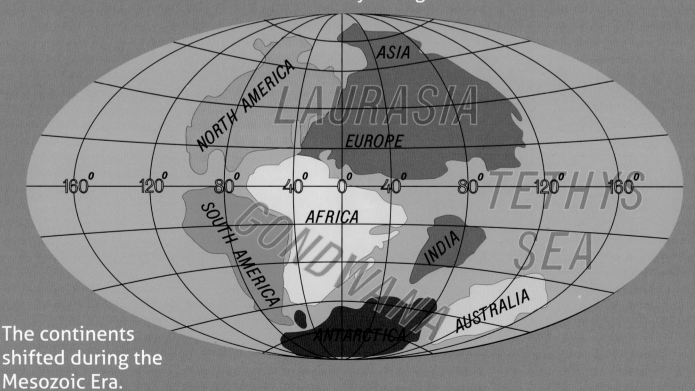

The continents shifted during the Mesozoic Era.

THE WORLD OF THE DINOSAURS

When dinosaurs first evolved, the Earth was very different from what it is today. All of the land on Earth formed one gigantic supercontinent, called Pangea (Pangaea). Over millions of years, the supercontinent broke up into separate landmasses that gradually resembled today's continents. Dinosaurs lived throughout this ancient world, in habitats ranging from tropical forests to dry, sandy deserts.

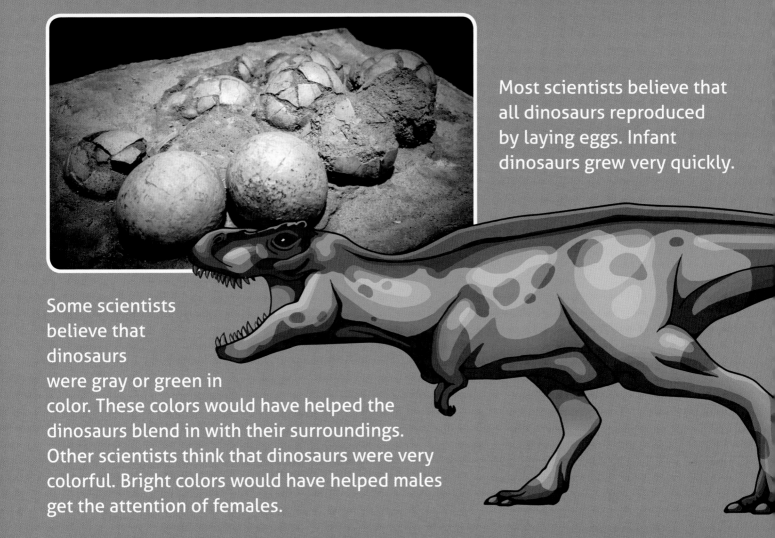

Most scientists believe that all dinosaurs reproduced by laying eggs. Infant dinosaurs grew very quickly.

Some scientists believe that dinosaurs were gray or green in color. These colors would have helped the dinosaurs blend in with their surroundings. Other scientists think that dinosaurs were very colorful. Bright colors would have helped males get the attention of females.

USE THE VR VIEWER AND ASSOCIATED APP

Enhance your experience by using the app! Put your smartphone in the VR viewer and you'll be able to find out more about North American dinosaurs and dinosaur digs!

DINOSAUR TYPES

All dinosaurs divided among two major orders: the Saurischia (lizard-hipped) and the Ornithischia (bird-hipped). Scientists classify dinosaur species into these orders based on their pelvic, or hip, structures.

SAURISCHIA

The order Saurischia includes both carnivorous and herbivorous dinosaurs who looked, behaved, moved, and foraged in very different ways.

Within the order Saurischia are two major subgroups—the theropods and the sauropodomorphs. The theropods were bipedal, meaning that they walked or ran on their two hindlimbs. They also were carnivorous, or meat-eating, predators that hunted prey. Among the best-known theropods are *Velociraptor*, *Allosaurus*, and *Tyrannosaurus rex*. Modern birds are closely related to this group. Most of the sauropodomorphs were quadrupedal, meaning that they stood and

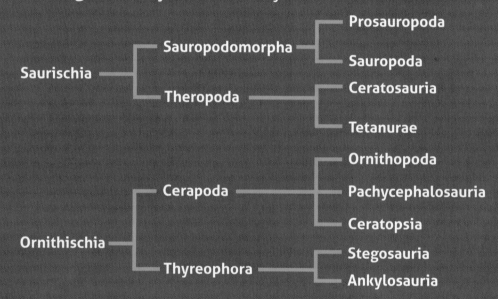

Saurischia
— Sauropodomorpha
  — Prosauropoda
  — Sauropoda
— Theropoda
  — Ceratosauria
  — Tetanurae

Ornithischia
— Cerapoda
  — Ornithopoda
  — Pachycephalosauria
  — Ceratopsia
— Thyreophora
  — Stegosauria
  — Ankylosauria

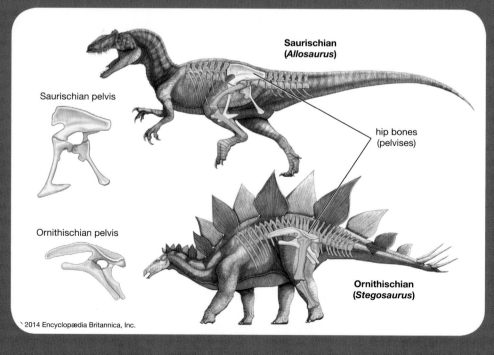

Saurischian pelvis

Saurischian
(*Allosaurus*)

hip bones
(pelvises)

Ornithischian pelvis

Ornithischian
(*Stegosaurus*)

© 2014 Encyclopædia Britannica, Inc.

walked on all four limbs. The sauropodomorphs were herbivorous, or plant-eating, dinosaurs that browsed the lush vegetation present during the Mesozoic era.

Baryonyx, a theropod, was a large, carnivorous, probably fish-eating dinosaur that inhabited England about 98 to 144 million years ago.

ORNITHISCIA

All members of the order Ornithischia were herbivores, or plant eaters. Most species had a toothless, horn-covered beak used to nip off vegetation. Also present were leaf-shaped cheek teeth, which were well adapted for grinding plant material. Yet another unique characteristic was muscular cheek pouches. These cheek pouches stored plant matter in the dinosaurs' mouths and prevented it from falling out as they chewed.

Some well-known ornithischians include the great horned dinosaurs, such as *Triceratops*, the armored dinosaurs, such as *Ankylosaurus*, and the plated dinosaurs, such as *Stegosaurus*.

Diplodocus, a sauropod, was an enormous herbivorous dinosaur that inhabited North America during the late Jurassic period.

THE TRIASSIC PERIOD

The Mesozoic ("middle life") era lasted from 252 million to about 66 million years ago. It is divided into three periods: the Triassic (252 million to 201 million years ago), the Jurassic (201 million to 145 million years ago), and the Cretaceous (145 to 66 million years ago).

THE EARLIEST DINOSAURS

The oldest known dinosaurs lived during the Triassic period. Among the oldest species known from this period were *Eodromaeus*, *Eoraptor*, and *Herrerasaurus*. All three were relatively small animals and lived in what is now South America. *Eodromaeus* and *Herrerasaurus* were carnivores, or meat eaters. *Eoraptor* may have eaten meat but also ate plants.

Eoraptor.

Herrerasaurus.

OTHER ANIMALS OF THE TRIASSIC

Therapsids (mammal-like reptiles) dominated animal life in the south, while primitive reptiles known as archosaurs were predominant in the north. The sea harbored an abundance of fish as well as newly evolved aquatic reptiles such as ichthyosaurs. The small shrewlike animals that were the first mammals also appeared late in the period. They are thought to have descended from the therapsids.

Therapsids such as *Lystrosaurus* were mammal-like reptiles that thrived early in the Triassic Period.

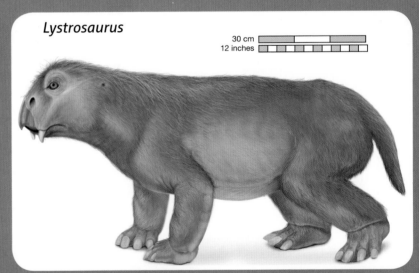

Lystrosaurus

30 cm
12 inches

END-TRIASSIC EXTINCTION

Scientists think that the mass extinction that occurred at the end of the Triassic Period (about 200 million years ago) may have been caused by rapid climate change or by an asteroid striking the Earth. This mass extinction event caused about 20 percent of marine families and some 76 percent of all species living at that time to die out. This vast loss of species opened up many ecological niches, paving the way for the evolution of the dinosaurs.

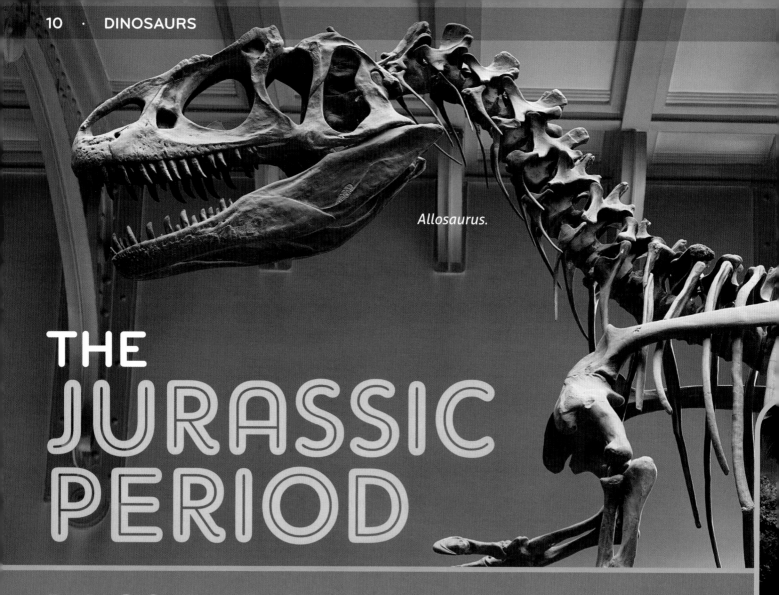

Allosaurus.

THE
JURASSIC
PERIOD

DINOSAURS OF THE JURASSIC

The dinosaurs greatly diversified in the Jurassic period. Some species reached enormous sizes, with plant-eating sauropods such as *Brachiosaurus* growing up to 40 feet (12 meters) tall and weighing up to 80 tons. The herbivores were preyed upon by carnivorous theropods such as *Allosaurus*. Some herbivores, such as *Stegosaurus*, developed self-defense features such as armored plates and bony spikes.

Conifers and ginkgos were common plants, and cycads were very abundant.

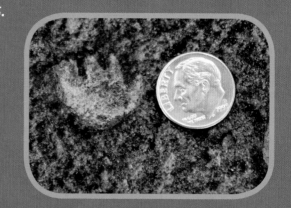

Scientists believe a small mammal left this track 190 million years ago in the area that is now Dinosaur National Monument.

BRACHIOSAURUS: FAST FACTS

1. *Brachiosaurus* ranks among the largest sauropods—and all land animals—that ever lived. It grew to approximately 75 feet (23 meters) in length and probably weighed between 55 and 66 tons.

2. It stood approximately 20 feet (6 meters) tall at the shoulders and its neck measured roughly 28 feet (8.5 meters) long, resulting in a total height of about 40 feet (12 meters).

3. Despite its size, scientists have speculated that it was capable of moving at speeds of about 12 to 19 miles per hour (19 to 31 kilometers per hour).

Brachiosaurus.

Archaeopteryx.

OTHER ANIMALS

The featherless flying and gliding reptiles called pterosaurs were common. *Archaeopteryx lithographica*, the oldest known animal that is generally accepted as a bird, first appeared in the late Jurassic. Mammals existed during this period as well but remained small.

THE
CRETACEOUS
PERIOD

OCEANS

During the Cretaceous period, thick deposits of chalk—the bodies of countless shell-producing marine organisms—were laid down in the shallow seas. Much of the deep ocean was largely devoid of life, though, as poor ocean circulation deprived the depths of oxygen. Large reptiles, such as plesiosaurs, swam in the sea.

The name Cretaceous is derived from the Latin word *creta*, meaning "chalk." This refers to a soft fine-grained limestone that was deposited in vast quantities during the late Cretaceous.

An artist's rendering of *Tyrannosaurs rex*.

Dinosaurs in general became even more diversified in the Cretaceous period. Important theropods of this period included the fearsome *Tyrannosaurus rex*, *Velociraptor*, and *Oviraptor*. Two of the best studied herbivorous dinosaurs of the Cretaceous were the armored *Ankylosaurus* and the great horned *Triceratops*.

OTHER ANIMALS

Flying reptiles such as the pterodactyls were common but declining in number, with the huge *Pteranodon* and *Quetzalcoatlus* remaining until the end of the period. Primitive birds continued to evolve from the theropod dinosaurs.

Fairly modern reptiles, such as crocodiles and turtles, are seen in Cretaceous strata. Mammals developed into all three of their current groups: placentals, marsupials, and monotremes. The dinosaurs still dominated, though, and mammals remained quite small.

The Cretaceous saw the first appearance of the angiosperms, or flowering plants. Members of the magnolia, laurel, sycamore, and rose families began to evolve during the Cretaceous period.

THE END OF AN ERA

The Cretaceous ended rather suddenly about 66 million years ago with a major extinction event that caused the end of the dinosaurs. This extinction is one of the worst known, with nearly 80 percent of all species destroyed.

SAUROPODOMORPHA

Sauropodomorpha consists of two groups of plant-eating dinosaurs—Prosauropoda and Sauropoda. The dinosaurs of Prosauropoda may have been the ancestors of those of Sauropoda. The dinosaurs of both these groups had a small head and a long and well-muscled neck. Most of them walked on four legs. The largest dinosaurs and the largest land animals ever to live were sauropods. Some grew to more than 100 feet (30 meters) in length.

PROSAUROPODS: FAST FACTS

1. Prosauropod fossils have been uncovered on every continent except Australia.

2. Prosauropods ranged in length from 5 to 30 feet (1.5 to 9 meters). Prosauropods lived during the period from the late Triassic into the early Jurassic.

3. The best studied prosauropod is *Plateosaurus*, a European herbivore that was 27 feet (8 meters) long and could walk on either two or four legs.

Plateosaurus.

SAUROPODS: FAST FACTS

1 Sauropod remains have been found in fossil beds dating from the late Triassic through the early Cretaceous periods—a time span of more than 100 million years.

2 Their true heyday was the mid-Jurassic period, roughly 180 million years ago.

3 Because of their size, most sauropods most likely had a distinct feeding advantage over other land-dwelling dinosaurs—their extremely long necks enabled them to browse among the tops of the tallest trees.

The family Camarasauridae contains smaller sauropods with shorter necks and tails than most other species. The most familiar member is *Camarasaurus*.

Gastroliths were stones that settled in the stomach and helped sauropods to grind up the tough plant material they consumed.

SAUROPODS IN THE SPOTLIGHT

Apatosaurus.

APATOSAURUS

Apatosaurus grew to about 70 feet (21 meters) in length, measured roughly 15 feet (4.6 meters) tall at the hips, and weighed an estimated 30 to 36 tons. Its relatively thick neck was about 20 feet (about 6.1 meters) long, but its head was small in relation to its body, measuring only 2 feet (61 centimeters) in length.

FAST FACTS

1. *Apatosaurus* may have traveled in herds.

2. Its diet is thought to have included the twigs and needles of sequoia, fir, and pine trees.

3. Its heavy, powerful tail was even longer than its neck.

Jobaria.

JOBARIA

A huge herbivorous dinosaur, *Jobaria* inhabited parts of Saharan Africa approximately 135 million years ago during the Cretaceous period (144–65 million years ago). A nearly complete (95 percent) skeleton was the first fossil evidence of *Jobaria*. It was discovered during a 1997 fossil-hunting expedition.

SEISMOSAURUS

Seismosaurus inhabited western North America during the late Jurassic period, approximately 159 to 144 million years ago. *Seismosaurus* may have been the longest species of dinosaur to ever exist. Fossil evidence shows that some individuals measured more than 150 feet (46 meters) long—equal to half the length of a U.S. football playing field. The dinosaur would have weighed approximately 100 tons or more, rivaling in size the largest living animal on Earth—the blue whale.

Seismosaurus.

THEROPODA

The Theropoda includes all carnivorous, or meat-eating, dinosaurs. The theropods ranged in size from the relatively small 100-pound (45-kilogram) *Velociraptor*, to the massive 6-ton *Tyrannosaurus rex*. Fossil evidence indicates that modern birds share a common ancestor with a branch of the theropods.

Afrovenator, a fearsome predator of the Cretaceous period (144–65 million years ago).

FAST FACTS

1. All theropods were bipedal, meaning that they stood upright and ran or walked on their two hind limbs.

2. Their legs were long and muscular.

3. Theropods had fairly short arms that ended in grasping hands armed with two or three clawed fingers.

4. Like modern birds, most species of theropods had hollow bones.

5. Theropods are most noted for the rows of razor-sharp teeth that lined their powerful jaws, enabling them to tear the flesh of their prey easily.

From the size of its massive skull, which measured approximately 5.4 feet (1.6 meters) long, paleontologists estimate that *Carcharodontosaurus* probably reached a length of more than 45 feet (13.7 meters).

CARNOSAURS AND TYRANNOSAURS

The most ferocious predators during the Jurassic period (approximately 201–145 million years ago) were the Carnosauria. The most notable carnosaur was *Allosaurus*, which appeared during the late Jurassic period, about 145 to 163 million years ago. It could reach a length of up to 39 feet (12 meters) and weighed approximately 1.5 tons.

By the late Cretaceous period, about 65 to 80 million years ago, carnosaurs were replaced by the tyrannosaurs. This group included the *Tyrannosaurus rex* ("tyrant lizard king").

Allosaurus.

THEROPODA:
SMALL BUT DANGEROUS

ORNITHOMIMUS

Ornithomimus was a small, birdlike dinosaur that inhabited North America and Asia about 65 to 98 million years ago during the late Cretaceous period.

FAST FACTS

1. *Ornithomimus* grew to about 12 feet (3.7 meters) in length and stood roughly 8 feet (2.4 meters) tall.

2. Although the head was light and small, the brain was large, earning *Ornithomimus* a reputation as one of the most intelligent of the dinosaurs.

3. *Ornithomimus* presumably was a swift runner, perhaps reaching speeds up to 30 miles per hour (48 kilometers per hour) while pursuing prey or escaping enemies.

4. *Ornithomimus* was probably omnivorous, consuming plants and fruit in addition to insects and small animals such as lizards.

Ornithomimus.

COMPSOGNATHUS

Compsognathus was a small, carnivorous dinosaur that inhabited Europe during the late Jurassic period, about 144 to 163 million years ago.

Compsognathus.

FAST FACTS

1. *Compsognathus* was one of the smallest of all dinosaurs, standing no higher than a chicken, and was similar in structure to *Archaeopteryx*, the first known bird.

2. The first fossil evidence of *Compsognathus* was an essentially complete skeleton discovered in Bavaria in southern Germany in the late 1850s. The remains of a young *Bavarisaurus*—a small, fleet lizard—were found in its stomach cavity.

OVIRAPTOR

Oviraptor was a small, carnivorous dinosaur that inhabited Asia during the late Cretaceous period, about 65 to 98 million years ago.

Oviraptor.

FAST FACTS

1. *Oviraptor* had a distinctive, lightweight skull unique among the dinosaurs. Its head resembled that of a parrot—deep and short with a toothless, stumpy beak.

2. The curved jaws were heavily muscled, providing the beak with the power to crush hard objects such as bones and mollusk shells.

THEROPODA:
BRAINS AND CLAWS

Velociraptor.

VELOCIRAPTOR

Velociraptor was an agile carnivorous dinosaur that inhabited Asia during the late Cretaceous period, approximately 65 to 99 million years ago.

FAST FACTS

1. *Velociraptor* was a small dinosaur, averaging only about 6 feet (2 meters) in length and weighing approximately 100 pounds (45 kilograms).

2. The quickness, agility, and lightweight body of *Velociraptor* made it one of the top predators of its time. Its large brain enabled it to make complex maneuvers when chasing prey.

3. *Velociraptor* preyed mainly upon herbivores that were smaller than itself. It also hunted in packs in order to bring down larger dinosaurs.

Deinonychus.

DEINONYCHUS

Deinonychus was a carnivorous dinosaur that inhabited North America during the early Cretaceous period, approximately 98 to 144 million years ago.

FAST FACTS

① As a predator, *Deinonychus* was built for the chase and the kill. Its body was strong and light; the average individual probably measured 10 feet (3 meters) in length and 6 feet (1.8 meters) in height and weighed only 150 pounds (68 kilograms).

② On each foot, the second of four toes had a long claw that was presumably used to slash through the flesh of prey. The claw measured up to 5 inches (13 centimeters).

TROODON

A small carnivorous dinosaur, *Troodon* inhabited North America during the late Cretaceous period, approximately 99 to 65 million years ago.

Troodon.

FAST FACTS

① Paleontologists consider *Troodon* to be among the most intelligent of dinosaurs.

② The most distinguishing feature of *Troodon* was its very large, partly forward-facing eyes. This unique adaptation may have enabled the animal to have binocular vision, or overlapping fields of vision, similar to that of modern humans.

THEROPODA:
LARGE PREDATORS
MEGALOSAURUS

Megalosaurus was a large, carnivorous dinosaur that inhabited Britain about 161 to 176 million years ago, during the Jurassic period. *Megalosaurus* was one of the first dinosaurs to be discovered in the early 1800s. When it was first described in 1824, it was given the name *Megalosaurus*, meaning "great lizard." *Megalosaurus* reached a length of about 30 feet (9 meters), a height of 10 feet (3 meters), and an estimated weight of one ton.

Megalosaurus.

CERATOSAURUS

Ceratosaurus was a large carnivorous dinosaur that inhabited North America about 144 to 163 million years ago during the late Jurassic period. *Ceratosaurus* was close in size to its relative *Allosaurus*, with some *Ceratosaurus* specimens reaching up to 30 feet (9 meters) in length and 6.5 feet (2 meters) in height. The most unusual feature of *Ceratosaurus* was a row of bony plates just below the skin along the top of the neck, body, and tail.

Ceratosaurus.

ALLOSAURUS

A large carnivorous dinosaur, *Allosaurus* was a fierce predator that inhabited North America and probably Africa, Australia, and Asia during the late Jurassic period, approximately 144 to 159 million years ago. *Allosaurus* grew up to 39 feet (12 meters) in length, weighed approximately 1.5 tons, and stood about 15 feet (4.5 meters) tall. Despite its size, paleontologists believe that *Allosaurus* was a speedy, agile predator capable of hunting down enormous herbivorous dinosaurs.

See *Allosaurus* in the VR app!

THEROPODA:
THE TITAN OF TERROR

The *Tyrannosaurus rex* was a large, carnivorous dinosaur that inhabited North America approximately 65 to 98 million years ago during the late Cretaceous period. The most widely recognized of all the dinosaurs, *T. rex* has inspired much speculation about how it lived, as well as what and how it ate.

A *T. rex* tooth.

A *T. rex* skull.

JUST THE STATS

The largest specimen ever found has a body length of 40 feet (12 meters) from head to tail and may have weighed more than four tons. The jaws were powerfully muscled, and the huge mouth contained two rows of serrated, pointed teeth. Many measured about 6 inches (15 centimeters) long, though some may have reached as much as 12 inches (30 centimeters) in length.

HUNTER OR SCAVENGER?

A good deal of scientific debate has focused on *T. rex*'s methods of obtaining prey. One school of thought is that it was a scavenger, an animal that searches for and consumes prey that is already dead.

A second group of researchers believe that *T. rex* was a true predator, capable of chasing down and killing its prey. This group cites the example of modern predators such as lions and hyenas, which scavenge carcasses when faced with no other choice but appear to prefer tracking down and consuming fresh meat.

Was *T. rex* a hunter or a scavenger? These illustrations depict very different possibilities.

CERAPODA: ORNITHOPODA

Scientists divide the Ornithischia into two suborders: the Thyreophora and the Cerapoda. The Cerapoda consists of three groups: Ornithopoda, Ceratopsia, and Pachycephalosauria.

The Ornithopoda includes the small heterodontosaurs and hypsilophodontids, the much larger iguanodonts, and the large duck-billed hadrosaurs.

IGUANODON

Iguanodon was a large, herbivorous dinosaur that inhabited North America, Europe, Africa, and Asia during the early Cretaceous period, about 98 to 144 million years ago.

Iguanodon grew to about 30 feet (9 meters) in length, stood over 15 feet (4.6 meters) tall, and probably weighed about 5 tons. It probably spent most of its time grazing on all four limbs but was capable of rearing up on its hind legs to browse in trees. Its head ended in a broad, toothless beak that it may have used to clip plant material, which was then pushed back for grinding by the blunt teeth in its powerful jaws. *Iguanodon*'s teeth resembled those of the modern iguana and inspired its name, which means "iguana tooth."

LESOTHOSAURUS

Lesothosaurus was a small, herbivorous dinosaur that inhabited Africa during the early Jurassic period, about 176 to 201 million years ago. *Lesothosaurus* was a small dinosaur, measuring just over 3 feet (0.9 meter) in length. The skull was small and flat-faced, resembling that of an iguana. The pointed teeth, which were shaped like small arrowheads, had grooved edges. The jaws were well adapted for dealing with tough vegetation.

CERAPODA:
ORNITHOPODA

Hypsilophodon.

HYPSILOPHODON

Hypsilophodon was a small, herbivorous dinosaur that inhabited Europe and North America during the early Cretaceous period, about 98 to 144 million years ago. *Hypsilophodon* grew to approximately 5 feet (1.5 meters) in length, stood about 3 feet (0.9 meter) tall, and weighed about 140 pounds (64 kilograms).

Fossil evidence suggests that the hypsilophodonts were social animals that lived in herds. Their lightweight bodies and long legs suggest that they were able to sprint from predators, earning them a reputation as the "gazelles" of the dinosaurs.

ORODROMEUS

Orodromeus was a small, herbivorous dinosaur that inhabited North America during the late Cretaceous period, about 65 to 98 million years ago.

The first fossil evidence of *Orodromeus* was discovered in the 1980s while a crew of paleontologists was examining nests of hadrosaur dinosaurs in Montana. At nearby sites, they discovered a large number of eggs of a new ornithopod dinosaur among the hadrosaur remains. The eggs and nests were remarkably well preserved; one complete nest contained 19 eggs laid in a precise spiral. The new dinosaur was named *Orodromeus*.

Orodromeus.

HETERODONTOSAURUS

Heterodontosaurus was a small, herbivorous dinosaur that inhabited areas of South Africa during the Jurassic Period, about 200 million years ago.

The distinguishing feature of *Heterodontosaurus* was its teeth, of which it had three different types. The first type of teeth were small and sharp and were located in the front of its top jaw. Its bottom jaw formed a horny beak in the front. The second type of teeth were long canine tusks that grew out of the top and bottom jaws. The third type of teeth were square-shaped cheek teeth in the back. With these different teeth, *Heterodontosaurus* could tear, bite, and grind its food.

Heterodontosaurus.

CERAPODA:
THE HADROSAURS

The Hadrosauridae are often called the duck-billed dinosaurs because the skulls of some species were broad and flat in front like a duck's bill. The hadrosaurs had rows of very tough teeth, as many as 500 to 2,000 teeth in the skull, depending on the species. The hadrosaurs can be divided into two groups—those with skull crests and those without. Both groups lived during the mid- to late Cretaceous.

A hadrosaur footprint in Colorado.

SHANTUNGOSAURUS

Shantungosaurus from China was the largest of the noncrested hadrosaurs. It was 49 feet (15 meters) long from its bill to the tip of its tail.

1 meter
3 feet

Maiasaura.

MAIASAURA

Studies of one of the best-known noncrested hadrosaurs, *Maiasaura*, have produced key insights about parental care among dinosaurs.

THE CRESTED HADROSAURS

The crested duck-billed dinosaurs were an unusual group of animals mainly from North America. They sported a variety of crests on the tops of their heads, through which the nasal passages passed. The crests may have functioned to amplify territorial or courtship calls.

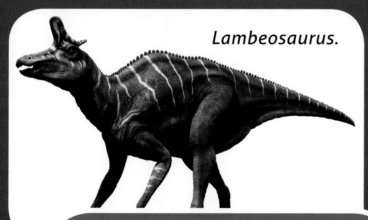

Lambeosaurus.

Parasaurolophus.

The name *Corythosaurus* means "helmet lizard."

Pachycephalosaurus.

CERAPODA:
CERATOPSIA AND PACHYCEPHALOSAURIA

PACHYCEPHALOSAURIA

The pachycephalosaurs are commonly called the bone-headed, or dome-headed, dinosaurs. Their name derives from their unusually thick skulls, which formed a rounded dome on their foreheads. Paleontologists once proposed that these domes enabled the animals to use their heads as battering rams in contests with one another, much in the way that modern bighorn sheep do. However, later studies revealed that the domes were inadequate for this task and were better adapted for butting rivals and adversaries in the flank. The largest pachycephalosaur was *Pachycephalosaurus*, which had a wall of bone over the top of its brain case that was 10 inches (25 centimeters) thick.

Psittacosaurus.

CERATOPSIA

The Ceratopsia are called the horned dinosaurs, though some of the earliest ceratopsids lacked horns. Ceratopsids lived during the Cretaceous period. All were herbivorous, and the fossil evidence suggests that most species lived in herds.

The human-sized bipedal *Psittacosaurus* from Mongolia, named for its unusual parrot-shaped head, was a hornless ceratopsid. Although they lacked horns, both *Leptoceratops* from western North America and *Protoceratops* from Asia had neck frills.

Protoceratops.

Scientists have long speculated about the function of the ceratopsids' horns and neck frills. Like modern horned mammals such as sheep and buffalo, the ceratopsids probably used their horns mainly in fights and displays with each other, as in contests for dominance or mates. Studies of the neck frills suggest that these functioned largely in regulating body temperatures.

CERATOPSIDS IN THE SPOTLIGHT

TRICERATOPS

The most famous ceratopsid was *Triceratops*. These dinosaurs were up to 30 feet (9 meters) long, weighed up to 6 tons, and had the largest heads of any land animals ever. *Triceratops* had a monstrous beak, dozens of teeth for grinding plants, three long sharp horns, and a thick shield of bone over the neck. *Triceratops* and its relatives probably lived in groups. They may have roamed like migrating herds of modern bison.

FAST FACTS

① Projecting from the massive skull of *Triceratops*—which measured more than 6 feet (2 meters) in length—were three sharp horns.

② The two upper horns, one projecting above each eye, reached a length of more than 3 feet (1 meter). The third horn projected from the animal's snout.

③ Fossil evidence strongly suggests these horns were used in harmless contests of strength—many of the neck frills found display scars where they had been scored by the horns of other *Triceratops*.

Centrosaurus was a large, herbivorous dinosaur that inhabited North America during the late Cretaceous period, approximately 65 to 98 million years ago.

Centrosaurus bone beds uncovered in the Canadian province of Alberta support the idea that this dinosaur may have grazed and traveled in herds.

THYREOPHORA

The dinosaurs of the subgroup Thyreophora were either plated or armored. Plated dinosaurs such as *Stegosaurus* had a double row of upright triangular bony plates running down the back. *Ankylosaurus* and other armored dinosaurs had flattened armor all over the top and sides of their bodies.

ANKYLOSAURUS

Ankylosaurus was a large armored dinosaur that inhabited North America approximately 70 million to 66 million years ago during the Late Cretaceous Period. It grew to a length of about 33 feet (10 meters) and weighed approximately four tons. The head, body, and tail were covered with bony plates set in leathery skin. Two sets of large spikes projected from the head, and rows of short spikes ran along the sides and tail. The tail, which was as long as the body, ended in a heavy "club" of bone, which it probably swung as a defense against predators.

Ankylosaurus.

SCELIDOSAURUS

An armored herbivorous dinosaur, *Scelidosaurus* inhabited parts of Europe during the early Jurassic period, approximately 206–180 million years ago.

Some paleontologists argue that it was a primitive stegosaur, and thus an early ancestor of the plated dinosaur *Stegosaurus*. Others suggest that it was more closely related to the ankylosaurs such as *Ankylosaurus*. Most experts agree, however, that *Scelidosaurus* was among the common ancestors of both groups.

Scelidosaurus.

EUOPLOCEPHALUS

Euoplocephalus was a large herbivorous dinosaur that inhabited North America during the Late Cretaceous Period, approximately 100 million to 66 million years ago. *Euoplocephalus* was a powerfully built tanklike creature that grew to about 20 feet (6 meters) in length and probably weighed more than two tons.

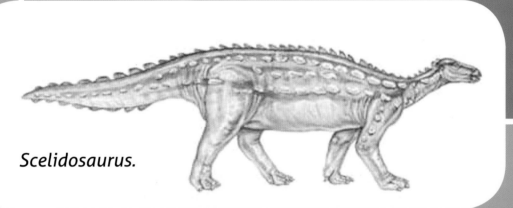

Euoplocephalus.

STEGOSAURUS
IN THE SPOTLIGHT

In the Jurassic period, the main group of armored dinosaurs was the Stegosauria. The most familiar of the stegosaurids is *Stegosaurus*.

WHAT WAS IT LIKE?

Stegosaurus normally reached an average length of 21 feet (6.5 meters), but some individuals grew to 30 feet (9 meters). *Stegosaurus* weighed approximately 2 tons and stood about 12 feet (3.7 meters) tall at the hips. The tail of *Stegosaurus* was armed with two pairs of spikes that measured up to 3 feet (1 meter) in length.

NOT THAT SMART

The skull and brain of *Stegosaurus* were especially small for such a large animal. Its narrow head measured only 16 inches (40 centimeters) long.

WHAT WERE THE PLATES FOR?

The most striking feature of *Stegosaurus* was the enormous line of triangular-shaped plates along its spine. Each horn-covered, bony plate stood more than 2 feet (60 centimeters) tall. There has been much debate as to the function of these plates. The alternating positions of the structures, which also contained several blood vessels, have led some paleontologists to believe that they were used to help the dinosaur control its body temperature. They could either act as solar panels to soak up the warmth of the sun, or they could help the animal to release excess body heat into the atmosphere. Other paleontologists believe that *Stegosaurus* used its plates for species recognition and for display purposes during the breeding season. One very likely function of these plates was to provide *Stegosaurus* with protection from predators such as *Allosaurus*.

DINOSAURS AND BIRDS

Many scientists believe that the closest dinosaur ancestors of birds belonged to a group of small carnivorous dinosaurs called coelurosaurs that evolved in the Jurassic period. Like modern birds, dinosaurs belonging to this group walked on their hind legs, and shared many other characteristics, such as long tails, three forward-pointing toes, and a similarly structured breastbone, or sternum.

DINOSAURS WITH FEATHERS

Several discoveries from the fossil-rich Liaoning Province in northeastern China provide strong support for a link between dinosaurs and birds. In the late 1990s a team of paleontologists discovered the fossil remains of three previously unknown dinosaurs that all had evidence of feathers.

In 2000, another expedition in Liaoning produced a small dinosaur that appeared even more closely related to birds. The crow-sized dinosaur, which scientists named *Microraptor zhaoianus*, lived in the late Jurassic or early Cretaceous periods.

MICRORAPTORS

Further excavations at the Liaoning site in 2002 produced specimens of another *Microraptor* species, which scientists named *M. gui*. Unlike previously discovered feathered dinosaurs, the *M. gui* specimens each had birdlike feathers on both hindlimbs and forelimbs. Experts propose that these four wings were well adapted for gliding.

An artist's rendering of microraptors.

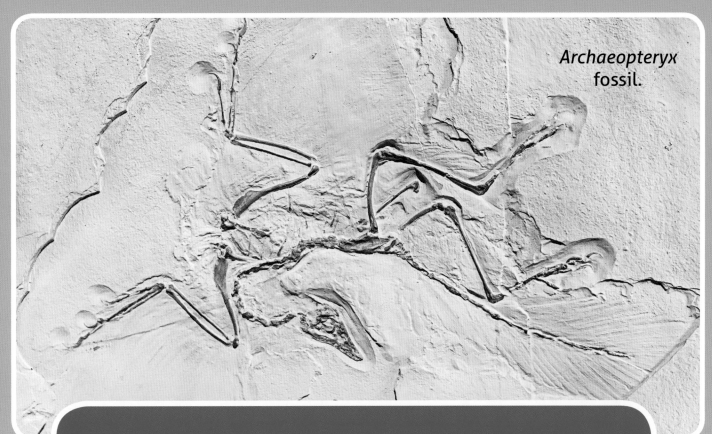

Archaeopteryx fossil.

ARCHAEOPTERYX

The famous Jurassic fossil of *Archaeopteryx* was once considered part dinosaur and part bird. Today scientists believe it was a true bird, perhaps one of the earliest known, and consider it a key link in the evolution between dinosaurs and birds. Recent discoveries in Liaoning have provided even closer links.

Archaeopteryx.

SHARING THE WORLD OF DINOSAURS

Although dinosaurs were the most spectacular animals of their day, they were by no means alone on the Earth. Other reptiles walked the land, flew through the air, and swam in the water. There were birds, mammals, and some odd creatures that were halfway between the reptile and the mammal.

Mosasaurs, giant lizards that ranged from 16 to 33 feet (5 to 10 meters) in length, never left the sea.

An artist's rendering of mosasaurs.

An ichthyosaur.

Ichthyosaurs, smaller reptiles that lived entirely in the ocean, looked very much like sharks.

Plesiosaurs were ocean-dwelling reptiles. Some species had very long necks and had flippers instead of legs.

An artist's rendering of a plesiosaur.

In the time of the dinosaurs, reptiles called pterosaurs sailed through the air. They glided from tree to tree and soared on air currents instead of actually flying, because they had no feathers. A typical representative was the pteranodon, which lived during the Cretaceous period, about 144 to 66.4 million years ago. One fossil pteranodon had a wingspan of 27 feet (8 meters).

Morganucodon is an extinct genus of tiny mammals that lived approximately 200 million years ago on the boundary between the Triassic and Jurassic geologic periods. *Morganucodon* was one of the earliest mammals.

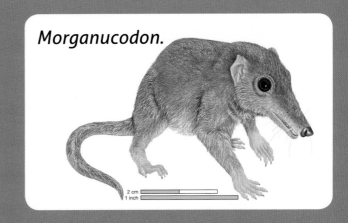

Morganucodon.

2 cm
1 inch

EXTINCTION

The Cretaceous ended rather suddenly about 66 million years ago with a major extinction event that caused the end of the dinosaurs. This extinction is one of the worst known, with nearly 80 percent of all species destroyed.

WHAT WAS THE CAUSE?

The causes of the Cretaceous extinctions have been greatly debated. Many scientists believe that a large asteroid, or rock from space, caused this mass extinction. When the asteroid hit Earth, the impact caused drastic changes.

AN INCREDIBLE IMPACT

The environmental consequences of such an event would have been severe. The energy of the impact is estimated to have been about 100 million megatons—the equivalent of 2 million of the most powerful nuclear bombs ever detonated. Huge tsunamis, earthquakes, and intense heat would have been almost immediate effects. The shock-heating of the air would have set off huge forest fires.

EFFECTS OVER TIME

Longer-term effects would have included an almost complete cutoff of sunlight reaching the ground over much of the world, lasting for months. Chemicals produced by the event could have poisoned the air and oceans. Carbon dioxide released by the vaporization of seafloor sediment could have caused a large greenhouse effect lasting hundreds of years afterward.

TROUBLESHOOTING

The image I see is blurry.

Make sure the smartphone is aligned precisely with the center of the viewer.
Adjusting the phone left or right a few millimeters can make a big difference.
The tilt of the viewer and the phone can also affect how the screen looks to you.
You can also try to calibrate the viewer using one of the QR codes found below.

I was asked to allow the app to take pictures.
Do I need to allow this?

Yes, this allows the app to take a picture of the QR code in your book in
order to validate your purchase and access the accompanying app.

How do I calibrate my viewer?

If asked to calibrate your viewer, scan the first of the QR codes found below. If the picture seems
blurry afterward, touch the small gear icon that appears at one corner of your screen. You will
then be given an opportunity to switch viewers. Scan the other QR code found here. Some
smartphones work better with one calibration, while others work better with the second.

I'm getting a pop-up that this app won't work without Google VR Services,
asking me to install it before continuing. Do I need to do this?

Click Cancel; it should not prevent you from running the app successfully.

Can I use this viewer with other apps?

The viewer is a standard size that is designed to be compatible with many apps. Try it out!

I damaged my viewer. Can I use this app with other viewers?

Yes, this app is compatible with many other standard-sized viewers on the market.

My screen gets dim when I place it in the viewer.

Check your phone settings. Under Display settings, if there is a setting such as "Auto adjust
brightness," where the screen adapts to lighting conditions, turn that setting off.